FAT CAT

Written by Nora Gaydos
Illustrated by BB Sams

innovativeKids®

A cat.

A tan cat.

A tan fat cat.

A tan fat cat ran.

A tan fat cat ran fast.

A tan fat cat is last.

A tan fat cat is sad.

CATS CLAP!

A tan fat cat is glad.

A tan fat cat has pals.

After You Read

Answer these questions about the story, and then use words from the story in fun, new ways!

1. What color is the cat?
   Why is the fat cat glad in the end?

2. What other words rhyme with *cat*?
   What other words rhyme with *ran*?
   What other words rhyme with *sad*?

3. Make up a different sentence of your very own for each of these words: *fast, clap, pal*.
   Now try to use all of those words together in *one* sentence!

Skills in This Story

Vowel sound: short *a*
Sight words: *a, is*
Word ending: *-s*
Initial consonant blends: *cl, gl*
Final consonant blend: *-st*

CRAB TRAP

Written by Nora Gaydos
Illustrated by BB Sams

The crab.

The bad crab.

The bad crab grabs.

The bad crab grabs ham.

The bad crab grabs
ham and jam.

The bad crab dabs
ham and jam on a trap.

BAM! WHAM!

The trap snaps.

The crab nabs a rat.

The rat is mad.

After You Read

Answer these questions about the story, and then use words from the story in fun, new ways!

1. What does the crab grab?
    Why is the rat mad?

2. What other words rhyme with *grab*?
    What other words rhyme with *trap*?
    What other words rhyme with *ham*?

3. Make up a different sentence of your very own for each of these words: *crab, jam, snap*.
    Now try to use all of those words together in *one* sentence!

Skills in This Story

Vowel sound: short *a*
Sight words: *the, and, on, a, is*
Word ending: *-s*
Initial consonant blends: *cr, gr, tr, sn*